BOOK 4

ter, Hampshire SO23 9HX

www.ransom.co.uk

ISBN   978 184167 410 0
First published in 2013
Copyright © 2013 Ransom Publishing Ltd.

Illustrations copyright © 2013 The Comic Stripper Ltd.

A CIP catalogue record of this book is available from the British Library.

The rights of H. L. Dube to be identified as the author and of The Comic Stripper to be identified as the Illustrator of this Work have been asserted by them in accordance with sections 77 and 78 of the Copyright, Design and Patents Act 1988.

STEVE SHARP

Finding Jo

by

H. L. Dube

Ransom

Steve Sharp

Steve was a cop. Now he works for himself. He is a hard man.

Jaydeen

Jaydeen works for Steve. She is in love with Steve, but never tells him.

Mrs Clayton

Mrs Clayton is rich. Her kid, Jo Clayton, is missing from home.

Jo Clayton

Jo left home to shack up with Big John, a drug dealer.

Big John

Big John makes big bucks selling drugs. He is a bad guy.

ONE

I have a job to do. To find Jo Clayton.

Seventeen years old and missing from home.

Last seen in the Doodle Club with Big John, drug dealer.

'Find her for me, Mr Sharp,' her mother begged me.

Sure, I will find Jo.

And Big John. That guy smacked me between the eyes.

So he has it coming to him.

Nobody plays with Steve Sharp and wins.

Nobody.

TWO

Two kids are in the street.

Sitting at the side of the road.

Sixteen or seventeen. Just kids.

They look bad.

They smell bad.

I get my wallet out.

I show them a twenty.

'You want it?' I say.

Their eyes tell me 'yes'.

'Do you know a guy with the name Big John?'

'He is the Man. I see him every day.'

'I must find him,'' I say.

'He is always at Park Street at five,' the kid says.

I give them the twenty.

Next time they will not be so lucky.

THREE

In the office, Jaydeen makes tea.

The way I like it. No milk. No sugar.

'Your face is OK now, Steve,'
Jaydeen says.

'Just give me the tea,' I say.

Jaydeen is a good kid.

'Take the day off, Jaydeen,' I say.

'Why?'

'I like you and you work hard. Go shopping.'

'Take care, Steve,' she says.

Later, I lock the office door.

I walk the streets of the city.

FOUR

This was a good place to live when I was a boy.

Now ... now it is a bad place.

I have lots of time. So I go to sit in a coffee shop.

I think of calling Val Foster, but I do not ring her.

Val is not my girl. She is with Frank
the Hat.

If I touch Val, Frank the Hat will kill
me.

I check the time. Soon be five.

I walk to Park Street.

The punters wait under the trees.

Lots of kids, all on drugs. Waiting for Big John.

Big John comes in a big car. A Jag.

He is alone. I do not see Jo Clayton.

John sells drugs to these poor kids.

I see no cops.

This is a bad city.

I make a note of the number of the car.

Then I call an old mate of mine.

We were cops in the old days and he is still a cop.

I give him the number of Big John's car.

He checks the computer and finds the street.

I walk down to a poor part of the city.

Number 5, Robin Street. This is the house. Big John's house.

STEVE SHARP

Now read
the next
Steve Sharp
book ....